ROOM ON THE BROOM
♫ and other songs ♫

For all at St. Michael on the Mount Primary School, Bristol – J.D.

First published 2006 by Macmillan Children's Books
This edition published 2007 by Macmillan Children's Books
an imprint of Pan Macmillan
20 New Wharf Road, London N1 9RR
Associated companies throughout the world
www.panmacmillan.com

ISBN: 978-1-4050-9101-5

9 11 13 12 10 8

A CIP catalogue record for this book is available from the British Library.

Printed in China

ROOM ON THE BROOM
and other songs

Julia Donaldson

Illustrated by Axel Scheffler

MACMILLAN CHILDREN'S BOOKS

Introduction

by Julia Donaldson

Welcome to my second book of songs for children. I was a songwriter long before I turned my hand to books, and I still love singing and playing my songs when I visit schools, theatres and book festivals.

Some of the songs in this collection are ones I wrote for children's television programmes. "Use Your Arms", "Shuffle and Squelch" and "Under the Water" are all action songs, and the suggested actions are pictured alongside the words and music. "The Crow and the Fox" and "The Dog and the Bone" are Aesop's Fables, which are fun for children to act out. "What's Your Colour?" is a celebration of the variety of human skin.

Once I started writing picture books, it felt natural to compose songs to go with them. Besides the "Room on the Broom" song, the book contains the companion songs to "The Smartest Giant in Town" and (my own favourite) "The Snail and the Whale".

All the songs have a simple piano accompaniment and guitar chords, but don't worry if you are not an instrument-player – there is a CD available which includes instrument-only (karaoke) tracks of all the songs so that children at home or school can sing along.

I am very grateful to Andrew Dodge for his inventive musical arrangements and also for rounding up the great musicians who play on the CD (Andrew himself plays the piano). Also to my busking partner and husband Malcolm, who plays the guitar and sings on some of the songs.

Finally, a big thank you to the one and only Axel Scheffler for his vivid and witty illustrations.

A note to accompanists by the musical arranger, Andrew Dodge:

As the tunes and their accompaniments are scored across two staves, there is often only a single line in the right-hand part (the treble clef) so that the sung melody is as clear as possible. Consequently, there are often notes written in the left-hand part (the bass clef) that are more easily played with the right hand. Please play the bass clef notes with whichever hand is easier.

Contents

Room on the Broom   2

Shuffle and Squelch   4

The Crow and the Fox   6

The Smartest Giant in Town   8

Use Your Arms   12

The Dog and the Bone   14

Under the Water   17

What's Your Colour?   20

The Snail and the Whale   22

Room on the Broom

Verse 1

I am a cat, as LEAN as can be.
Is there room on the broom for
a cat like me?

Yes, yes, yes!

Verse 2

I am a dog, as KEEN as can be.
Is there room on the broom for
a dog like me?

Yes, yes, yes!

Verse 3

I am a bird, as GREEN as can be.
Is there room on the broom for
a bird like me?

Yes, yes, yes!

Verse 4

I am a frog, as CLEAN as can be.
Is there room on the broom for
a frog like me?

Yes, yes …

No!

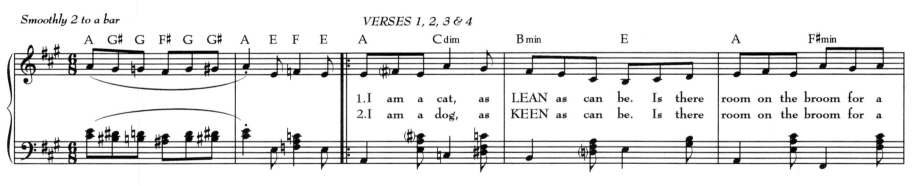

Verse 5

I am a dragon, as MEAN as can be.
Is there room on the broom for a dragon
    like me?

NO, NO, NO!

OFF YOU GO!

Ho ho ho ho ho ho ho HO!

Shuffle and Squelch

Verse 1
Spring brings showers; the world's aflood.
Wellies on, let's brave the mud.
We'll go squelching about, squelching about,
Squelching about in the mud.
Yes, we'll go squelching about, squelching about,
Squelching about in the mud.

Verse 3
Hold your hat, the winds are thieves.
Watch them steal the autumn leaves.
As we shuffle about, shuffle about,
Shuffle about in the leaves.
Yes, we can shuffle about, shuffle about,
Shuffle about in the leaves.

Verse 2
Kick your boots off, everyone.
Summer's here and so's the sun.
We'll go dancing about, dancing about,
Dancing about in the sun.
Yes, we'll go dancing about, dancing about,
Dancing about in the sun.

Verse 4

Wind your scarf round once or twice,
Winter's turned the pond to ice.
We'll go sliding about, sliding about,
Sliding about on the ice.
Yes, we'll go sliding about, sliding about,
Sliding about on the ice.

The Crow and the Fox

Verse 1

Fox on the ground, Crow in the trees.
Fox feeling hungry, Crow has some cheese.
Fox licks his lips, "Good morning, hello.
How do you do, you beautiful crow?"

Chorus

Hush, silly bird, don't open your beak.
You'll lose that cheese if you speak.

Verse 2

Fox tries again, "Beautiful day,
Don't you agree? What do you say?
Elegant bird with feathers so sleek,
Can you be dumb? Why don't you speak?"

Chorus

Verse 3

"Your wings and your tail are glossy and dark.
Your eyes are like diamonds, your voice like a lark.
Sing for me now! Oh, how I long
To hear just one note – won't you sing me a song?"

Chorus

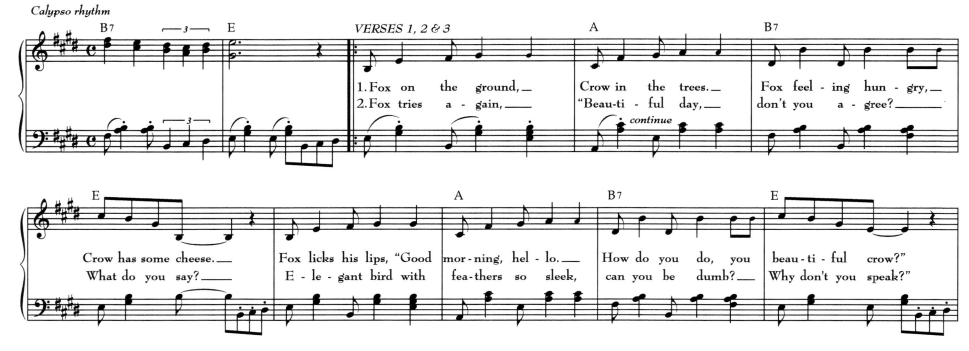

repeat x2 for verses 2 & 3

Verse 4

Crow feeling good, puffing with pride,
Eyes shining brightly, head on one side,
Opens her beak, lets out a sound – CAAAGH!
Down falls the cheese to Fox on the ground.

Hush, silly bird, why did you croak?
You lost that cheese when you spoke.

Fox on the ground, Crow in the trees,
Crow feeling hungry, Fox has the cheese.

The Smartest Giant in Town

The first five verses are sung by George, the giant.

Verse 1
My tie is a scarf for a cold giraffe,
But look me up and down –
I'm the smartest giant in town.

Verse 2
My tie is a scarf for a cold giraffe,
My shirt's on a boat as a sail for a goat,
But look me up and down –
I'm the smartest giant in town.

Verse 3
My tie is a scarf for a cold giraffe,
My shirt's on a boat as a sail for a goat,
My shoe is a house for a little white mouse,
But look me up and down –
I'm the smartest giant in town.

Verse 4
My tie is a scarf for a cold giraffe,
My shirt's on a boat as a sail for a goat,
My shoe is a house for a little white mouse,
One of my socks is a bed for a fox,
But look me up and down –
I'm the smartest giant in town.

Verse 5

My tie is a scarf for a cold giraffe,
My shirt's on a boat as a sail for a goat,
My shoe is a house for a little white mouse,
One of my socks is a bed for a fox,
My belt helped a dog who was crossing a bog,
But . . . my trousers are falling down!
I'm the coldest giant in town!

With a gently lumbering beat

1. My tie is a scarf for a cold gi-raffe, but look me up and down – I'm the smar-test gi-ant in town. 2. My

tie is a scarf for a cold gi-raffe, my shirt's on a boat as a sail for a goat, but look me up and down – I'm the smar-test gi-ant in town. 3. My

tie is a scarf for a cold gi-raffe, my shirt's on a boat as a sail for a goat, my shoe is a house for a lit-tle white mouse, but look me up and

down — I'm the smar-test gi-ant in town.— 4.My tie is a scarf for a cold gi-raffe, my shirt's on a boat as a sail for a goat, my

shoe is a house for a lit-tle white mouse, one of my socks is a bed for a fox, but look me up and down — I'm the smar-test gi-ant in

town.— 5.My tie is a scarf for a cold gi-raffe, my shirt's on a boat as a sail for a goat, my shoe is a house for a lit-tle white mouse,

one of my socks is a bed for a fox, my belt helped a dog who was cros-sing a bog, but my trou-sers are fal - ling down! I'm the

This last verse is sung by all the animals.

Verse 6

Your tie is a scarf for a cold giraffe,
Your shirt's on a boat as a sail for a goat,
Your shoe is a house for a little white mouse,
One of your socks is a bed for a fox,
Your belt helped a dog who was crossing a bog,
So here is a very fine crown
To go with the sandals and gown
Of the KINDEST giant in town.

Use Your Arms

Verse 1

Use your arms like a policeman:
make the traffic stop and go.

Use your arms like an archer:
shoot an arrow from your bow.

Use your arms like a strongman,
lifting up a heavy weight.

Use your arms like a scarecrow:
stick them out all stiff and straight.

Chorus

Stretch, shrug,
Fold, hug:
Use your arms.
Use your arms.
(*After last verse:* Use your arms.)

Smoothly and evenly

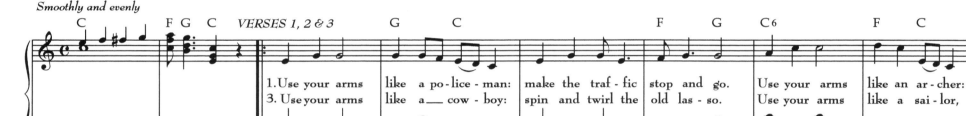

VERSES 1, 2 & 3

1. Use your arms | like a po-lice-man: | make the traf-fic | stop and go. | Use your arms | like an ar-cher:
3. Use your arms | like a— cow-boy: | spin and twirl the | old las-so. | Use your arms | like a sai-lor,

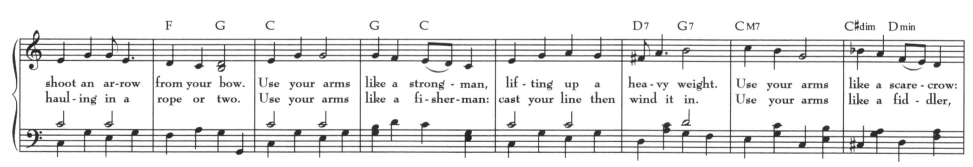

shoot an ar-row | from your bow. | Use your arms | like a strong-man, | lif-ting up a | hea-vy weight. | Use your arms | like a scare-crow:
haul-ing in a | rope or two. | Use your arms | like a fi-sher-man: | cast your line then | wind it in. | Use your arms | like a fid-dler,

Copy these actions for the chorus:

Stretch your arms.

Shrug your shoulders.

Fold your arms.

Hug yourself.

12

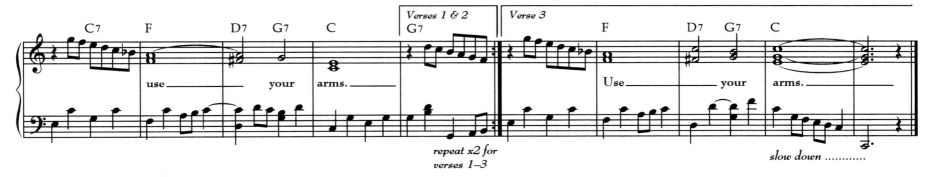

repeat x2 for
verses 1–3

slow down ....

Verse 2

Use your arms like a mother:
rock your baby son or daughter.

Use your arms like a diver,
poised to plunge into the water.

Use your arms like a swimmer:
do the breast stroke, do the crawl.

Use your arms like a bowler,
running up to throw the ball.

Chorus

Verse 3

Use your arms like a cowboy:
spin and twirl the old lasso.

Use your arms like a sailor,
hauling in a rope or two.

Use your arms like a fisherman:
cast your line, then wind it in.

Use your arms like a fiddler,
playing on your violin.

Chorus

13

The Dog and the Bone

Verse 1

Under a clear blue sky,
On a steep green bank,
A small black dog is gnawing a big white bone.
He wags his tail
And bows his head
And there in the pond, sitting all on his own,
Under a clear blue sky,
On a steep green bank,
Is a small black dog, gnawing a big white bone.

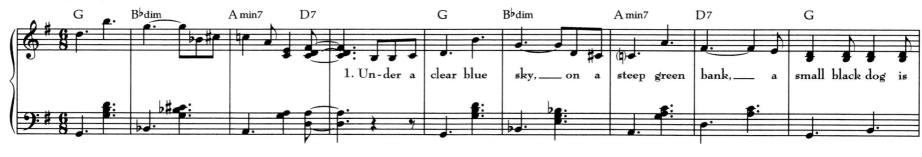

14

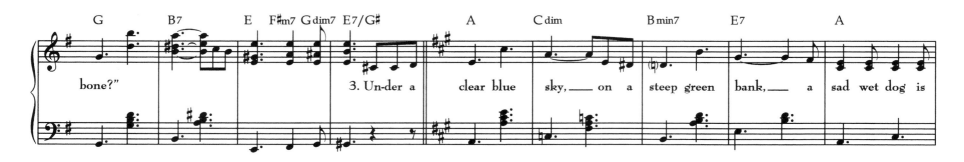

Verse 2

Says the dog on the bank
To the dog in the pond,
"I want your bone as well as my own, so there!"
He jumps right in,
But soon climbs out.
"I'm cold and wet and I've lost my bone, and where
Was the clear blue sky
And the steep green bank
And the small black dog gnawing the big white bone?"

Verse 3

Under a clear blue sky,
On a steep green bank,
A sad wet dog is missing his big white bone.
He droops his tail
And bows his head
And there in the pond, sitting all on his own,
Under a clear blue sky,
On a steep green bank,
Is a sad wet dog missing his big white bone.

 # Under the Water

Verse 1
Fish blow bubbles under the water.
Here's how the fish blow bubbles under the water.
Why don't you swim underwater with me?
Look through your goggles and see
How the fish blow bubbles under the water,
Down below.

Verse 2
Tadpoles wriggle under the water.
Here's how the tadpoles wriggle under the water.
Why don't you swim underwater with me?
Look through your goggles and see
How the tadpoles wriggle
And the fish blow bubbles under the water,
Down below.

Verse 3
Seaweed flutters under the water.
Here's how the seaweed flutters under the water.
Why don't you swim underwater with me?
Look through your goggles and see
How the seaweed flutters
And the tadpoles wriggle
And the fish blow bubbles under the water,
Down below.

Verse 4

Sharks eat fishes under the water.
Here's how the sharks eat fishes under the water.
Why don't you swim underwater with me?
Look through your goggles and see
How the sharks eat fishes
And the seaweed flutters
And the tadpoles wriggle
And the fish blow bubbles
Under the water, down below.

Verse 3

C G/B F/A G7 | C G/B F/A G7 | C G/B F/A C/G | G7 | F | C

sea-weed | flut-ters and the | tad-poles | wrig-gle and the | fish blow | bub-bles un-der the | wa-ter, | | down__ be-low.__

Verse 4

C G/B F/A G7 | C G/B F/A G7 | C G/B F/A G7 | C G/B F/A C/G | G7 | F | C

sharks eat | fish-es and the | sea-weed | flut-ters and the | tad-poles | wrig-gle and the | fish blow | bub-bles un-der the | wa-ter, | | down be-low.__

Copy these actions for each verse:

Verse 1: puff your cheeks in and out.

Verse 2: wriggle all over.

Verse 3: wave your arms in the air.

Verse 4: open your arms and snap them together like jaws.

Add your own verses and think up appropriate actions
e.g. "Crabs can nip you".

What's your Colour?

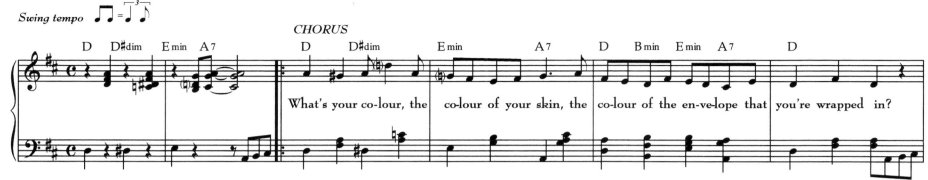

Swing tempo

CHORUS

What's your co-lour, the | co-lour of your skin, the | co-lour of the en-ve-lope that | you're wrapped in?

Chorus

What's your colour, the colour of your skin,
The colour of the envelope that you're wrapped in?

Verse 1

Is it like chocolate, tea or coffee?
Is it like marzipan, fudge or toffee?
Peaches and cream or a strawb'ry milkshake?
Or covered in moles like a curranty cake?

Chorus

Verse 2

Are you a map of your past disasters?
Grazes and scratches and sticking plasters?
Bites from mosquitoes, a yellow-blue bruise?
And a couple of blisters from rather tight shoes?

Chorus

Verse 3

How does it go when the weather's sunny?
Brown as a berry or gold as honey?
Does it go freckly or peeling and sore?
Is there a mark from the watch that you wore?

Chorus

Verse 4

Do you go pink when you're all embarrassed?
Sweaty and red when you're hot and harassed?
Bumpy and blue on a cold winter's day?
When it's time for your bath are you usually grey?

Chorus

The Snail and the Whale

Verse 1
This is the tale,
The incredible tale of a snail and a whale.
This is the tale,
The incredible tale of a snail
Who sailed all round the world on the tail of a whale.

Verse 2
Land, sea and sky.
It was all so enormous it made the snail sigh.
Land, sea and sky.
"Oh, how terribly tiny am I,
"Oh, how tiny am I," said the snail with a sigh.

Verse 3
Then came the day
When the whale lost his way and was beached in a bay.
Then came the day
When the water was slipping away
And he heavily, helplessly lay in the bay.

Slow, steady pace

1. This is the tale,____ the in-cre-di-ble tale of a snail and a whale. This is the
2. Land, sea and sky.____ It was all so e-nor-mous it made the snail sigh. Land, sea and

(continue)

tale,__ the in-cre-di-ble tale of a snail__ who sailed all round the world on the tail____ of a whale.
sky.__ "Oh, how ter-ri-bly ti-ny am I!____ Oh how ti-ny am I!" said the snail____ with a sigh.

repeat x5 for verses 2–6

last time slow down - - - - - - - - -

Verse 4

Here comes the snail.
Keep your eyes on the blackboard – she's leaving a trail.
Here comes the snail
And she writes on the board, "Save the whale."
"Save the whale," writes the snail with her silvery trail.

Verse 5

Dig, squirt and spray.
All the children and firemen are working away.
Dig, squirt and spray,
Till the tide rolls back into the bay
And the snail and the whale travel safely away.

Verse 6

Snail after snail
After snail slithers on to the tail of the whale.
Snail after snail
And they sing to the sea as they sail,
Yes, they sing as they sail on the tail of the whale.

23